Mommy &
Are Not Together
AND I'm OK!
MW00948905
Written By
Nykia Ward
Illustrated By
Andre Sullivan

Copyright © 2020 Nykia Reche' Ward

All rights reserved. No part of this publication may be reproduced, distributed, or transmitted in any form or by any means, including photocopying, recording, or other electronic or mechanical methods, without the prior written permission of the publisher, except in the case of brief quotations embodied in critical reviews and certain other noncommercial uses permitted by copyright law. For permission requests, write to the publisher, addressed "Attention: Permissions Coordinator," at the address below.

ISBN: 978-0-578-81175-8
Library of Congress Control Number: 2020923538

Printed by Prize Publishing House, LLC in the United States of America.
First printing edition 2020.
Prize Publishing House
P.O. Box 9856 Chesapeake, VA 23321
www.PrizePublishingHouse.com

Front cover image by Jamaal Williams
Illustrated by Andre' Sullivan

This book is dedicated to my girls:
Keera & Kaycee.

Defy the odds, overcome the obstacles,
change the perception!
You are loved and you are cherished!

Love you Forever and Always !

-Mom

*"For you created my inmost being;
you knit me together in my mother's womb.
I praise you because I am fearfully and wonderfully made;
your works are wonderful,
I know that full well." Psalms 139:13-14 (NLT)*

Mommy and Daddy love me and
this I cannot lie...
2 pairs of arms to hug,
4 ears to listen, and 2 shoulders
on which I can cry.

#1
MOM
#1
DAD

I have a home away from home,
summer visits are fun indeed.
Away with my cousins, run
errands with grandma, or lay
around with a good book to read.

Mommy takes me shopping, late night jokes on the phone with dad makes me laugh.
I am surrounded near and far by people who love me. If I tried, I could not tell you the half.

Mommy and Daddy love me and
this I cannot lie...
2 pairs of arms to hug,
4 ears to listen, and 2 shoulders
on which I can cry.

I split my fun in two, with Mom
and Dad alike.
Out for ice cream, late night
movies, or learning new things
like how to ride a bike.

Things are brand new! It won't
be all bad, just wait and see...
I know this from experience.
Look how we are doing.
Look at my sister and me!

12
1
2
3
4
5
6
7
8
9
10
11

Mommy and Daddy love me and
this I cannot lie...
2 pairs of arms to hug,
4 ears to listen, and 2 shoulders
on which I can cry.

You may feel sad at times, my
little friend, but don't cry. You
are surrounded by love and
family.
Smile!  Look up!
Don't let the good moments pass
you by.

## AFFIRMATIONS FOR YOUR CHILD

You are smart!

You are funny!

You are beautiful/handsome!

You were born with purpose!

## AFFIRMATIONS FOR YOUR CHILD

You will defy the odds!

You will rise above negativity!

You can be anything you want to be!

You are happy, healthy, & whole!

**You are loved!**

# ABOUT THE AUTHOR

Nykia Ward –
Daughter of William N. Ward Jr. and
(the late) Florine E. Cypress Ward,
Mother of Keera and Kaycee,
Sister, Niece, Cousin, Friend,
Special Education Teacher.

CPSIA information can be obtained
at www.ICGtesting.com
Printed in the USA
LVHW021557080121
675967LV00009B/612